Contents

Introduction

These worksheets are designed for use with Key Stage 2 pupils studying the 'Victorian Britain' unit.

The Victorian Age, from 1837–1901, saw many changes in the industrial, social, political and cultural life of Britain. The rise of industrialism led to the growth of the industrial cities. The need to produce a vast array of goods for domestic and overseas markets resulted in many unsafe, unsanitary factories where people worked very long hours for very poor pay. During the Victorian period various Factory Acts reduced the ages at which women and children could work in textile mills, factories and mines. In 1833 a Factory Act reduced the working day for children aged 9–13 to nine hours a day. By 1901 the minimum age at which a child could work was raised to 12. Trade unions developed to make sure that workers were given a fair deal.

Agriculture declined during this period, and the labourers needed to carry out the traditional farming tasks were replaced in some instances by new steam-driven farm machinery. However, it must be remembered that such machines were expensive and only the well-off landowners could afford to buy their own. In many areas the agricultural labourer remained an important, although very undervalued and underpaid, member of the community.

Those people who could not work became part of the rigid 'care' system in which the workhouse regime was often worse than prison. Fear of the workhouse was a feature of life for the labouring classes. Yet those with money enjoyed a good lifestyle during the Victorian Age. Even many lower-middle-class households had a maid. The large houses had a considerable number of domestic servants who, like their industrial counterparts, worked long hours for little money, but without the support of any trade union. This reliance on domestic servants did not decline until World War I.

The transport system provided better communications between towns, cities and countries in the Empire. So, too, did the development of the postal service (1840); letters could now be carried by train. By the end of Victoria's reign some people were using telephones, which were invented in 1876. The railway network made it possible for ordinary people to travel to different parts of the country. With the introduction of bank holidays in 1871, more people began taking short holidays, or day excursions to the seaside. There was a resultant rise in boarding houses and cheaper hotels.

The Victorian Age also saw an improvement in basic education and health provision. At the beginning of Victoria's reign many schools were simply Sunday schools which began to open during the week. These became known as National Schools and their objective was to teach children the Bible. In 1846 the pupil-teacher system was introduced, and in 1870 the Forster Education Act introduced state education and established School Boards. The Victorian education system concentrated heavily on the three 'Rs' of Reading, wRiting and aRithmetic, and in church schools there was the additional 'R' of Religion. In 1899 education became compulsory for all children up to 12 years old.

Throughout the nineteenth century there was an increasing awareness of the need for basic hygiene. This was given new significance with the epidemics of diseases such as cholera, which struck industrial areas with poor sanitation. Various Sanitary Acts and Health Acts attempted to clean up towns and rivers, avoid overcrowding towns and generally improve conditions.

Above all, the Victorian Age was a period of vast and accelerated change.

USING THE WORKSHEETS

The majority of these worksheets are designed to be used by pupils working on their own, although several are intended for use by pupils working in small groups. It is assumed that they will have access to the information on the sheets, and to other support material provided by the teacher.

A **Glossary** sheet is provided on page 7, and pupils should complete this as they work through the worksheets.

Worksheet 1: Using the census

The aim of this worksheet is to introduce pupils to an important primary source and to help them to gather information by careful reading of historical sources.

Explain to the pupils that, since 1801, the census has been sent to households every ten years, except in 1941 when World War II was taking place. It is a very useful source for historians, as it provides information about the jobs people did, the number of people who lived in the same house, their ages and also how far away people moved from the place where they were born. The public is not allowed to see the census for 100 years after the information is gathered. So the most recent census historians can use is the 1891 census. Explain to the children that 'Do' means 'ditto' or 'the same' (or ask them to find out the meaning for themselves). The **answers** to the questions are: **1** 3 Southend Road, Bradfield; **2** 8; **3** Millson; **4** 3; **5** Bricklayer; **6** He is described as a widower; **7** No – it was expected that the eldest daughter would run the home if there was no mother to do the job; **8** They are twins; **9** 14.

Worksheet 2: Planning the census

Pupils should work in groups of three for this worksheet. Having worked out the questions they need to ask, they could use IT to design their census.

Worksheet 3: Street directories

Again, the aim of this sheet is to encourage pupils to look closely at written sources, and to introduce a different example of a primary source available to historians. The **answers** to the questions are: **1** John Weir; **2** 4; **3** Joseph Spence, Patrick Birnie, Angus M'Donald, William Rose; **4** He collected and recycled cloth; **5** Making new cloth and making paper; **6** Temperance hotel – a hotel that did not sell alcohol; drysalter – dealt in drugs, dyes, gums, oils, pickles and tinned meats.

Worksheets 4A and 4B: Changes

The worksheet introduces the idea that historians can use primary sources to chart the changes in a locality over time. The **answers** to the questions are: **1** 4; **2** 6; **3** 1881 census; **4** Use the 1881 census; **5** Fort Corinthian Yacht Club; **6** On the coast – the jobs people do include boatman, shore dues collector, customs official and ship's carpenter; **7** Her Majesty's Customs.

Worksheets 5A and 5B: The labourer's life

This is a comprehension exercise. The **answers** to the questions are: **1** Brick and stone were very expensive materials; **2** Bricks began to be mass produced ; **3** 14.2 per cent; **4** Life was becoming very difficult – they had little money and food; **5** In the towns, where the factories were creating new jobs; **6** Steam-powered machinery; **7** The landlord; **8** His home; **9** To prevent the birds from eating the seed, which was scattered by hand on the surface. It was also a good way for a family to earn some extra money.

Worksheet 6: Counting the pennies

This worksheet emphasizes the difficulties agricultural labourers faced in 'making ends meet'. The **answers** to the questions are: **1** 240 weeks (4 weeks to save 1d, 12 x 4 weeks to save 1 shilling = 48 weeks, 5 x 48 weeks to save 5 shillings); **2** Soap was used for all cleaning – personal washing, laundry and household cleaning; **3** They were cheap and filling; **4** 50.848 kg.

Worksheets 7A and 7B: Village trades

These worksheets offer a further opportunity for work with written sources, and indicate the range of occupations in a Victorian village. Many villages were more or less self-sufficient. The carrier, who served several villages, would be asked to bring from the local town tools or materials that could not be obtained in the village. The **answers** to the questions are: **1** 129/1000 = 12.9 per cent; **2** As there is a rector and a Methodist minister in the village, there are probably 2; **3** Fly – small carriage pulled by one horse; farm bailiff – the equivalent of a modern farm manager; draper – sold cloth; woodsman – looked after the forest; **4** 1 teacher to 35.4 pupils; **5** Pupil answer; **6** 12.5 per cent.; **7** Pupil answer.

Worksheet 8: Workhouse life

This worksheet is designed for use by pupils working in groups of three or four. It provides a stimulus for wider research, and practice in selecting, organizing and presenting material. Pupils could present their scripts to the class if access to a tape recorder is difficult to arrange.

Worksheet 9: The growing towns
This worksheet encourages pupils to think about the practicalities of life for Victorian factory workers. It can also be used as an introduction to Worksheet 10.

Worksheets 10A, 10B, 10C: Town planning
This exercise is designed to help pupils to think about the effect that the rapid, unplanned growth of the factory towns had on the living conditions of the factory workers. The work is intended to be spread over two sessions. **You should enlarge the base map on Worksheet 10A to A3 size.** The questions on Worksheet 10C could be used for a class discussion, rather than a written exercise.

Worksheet 11: Servants wanted
This worksheet encourages pupils to think about what life was like for domestic servants, and provides opportunities to write for different purposes: a letter and an advertisement.

Worksheet 12: The cook's day
As well as providing details about the duties of a cook, this sheet offers an opportunity for pupils to think about the way information is presented, through pictures, speech bubbles, captions, etc.

Worksheets 13A and 13B: Education for all?
This worksheet gives an idea of the range of different types of schooling available in the Victorian period. The **answers** to the questions are: 1 Poor children only needed a very basic education to get by in everyday life; 2 It was better for his business to have an educated workforce, even though the education provided was very basic; 3 Religion; 4 They didn't want their children to mix with the lower classes and could also control what their children were taught by having them taught at home; 5 Girls were educated to run a household and entertain – skills a husband would expect! They were expected to look after the home and raise children, not to have a working life outside the home. It was not 'expected' that girls would go to university. Pupils could use IT to design their prospectuses.

Worksheet 14: School log books
This worksheet introduces another type of written source – the school log book – and offers further practice in the use of written sources to extract information. Explain to the pupils that, after 1870, headteachers were required to record in the log book events that took place in the school, and also events in the local area that affected the school. The **answers** to the questions are: 1 Children walked to school, and for some this would have been a long walk across muddy fields and through woods. In bad weather it was impractical for them to attend. 2 The hay had to be got in quickly, before bad weather could spoil it, so as many people as possible were needed to help. It was also a good way for children to earn extra money. 3 Measles was very infectious and a killer; 4 Doctors tried to prevent the spread of the disease by isolating the sick and reducing everyday contact between people who might be incubating the illness. 5 A lamp was used to project images from coloured or black-and-white glass slides on to a wall. Today it would be called a slide projector. It was obviously popular because 200 people attended the village performance.

As an extension, pupils could use the information here and other reference books to find out what a day or week in the life of a Victorian school would have been like. They could present their findings in the form of a newspaper article.

Worksheet 15: Going to church
This worksheet indicates the different forms of worship favoured by the different classes, and the importance of religion in children's lives. The **answers** to questions are: 1 Services were often geared towards the middle and upper classes, who sat at the front, sometimes in their own private pews; 2 Because they could not read; 3 It was the only education some of them received.

Worksheet 16: Tickets to ride
This worksheet offers an opportunity for pupils to practise their maths, and illustrates the tight budgets on which the poor lived. The **answers** to the questions are: 1 150 pennies (12/6); 2 124 weeks per person; 3 Modesty in relation to clothes was very important; people did not want to be seen even partially undressed.

Worksheets 17A and 17B: Planning Seathorpe
If possible, enlarge the map to A3 size. Pupils should work in groups of three or four. These worksheets encourage pupils to think about the range of facilities that are needed in a holiday resort. Pupils should gain an understanding of the massive changes that quiet seaside towns and villages underwent with the arrival of the railways and day trippers. Once they have completed their maps and posters, pupils could present their ideas to the class for discussion.

Worksheet 18 Revision wordsearch
The **answers** to the wordsearch questions are: 1 Australia, New Zealand; 2 Emigrants; 3 Board, Ragged; 4 Landlord; 5 Agricultural labourers; 6 Manchester; 7 Street directories; 8 Census; 9 Hundred years; 10 Workhouse; 11 Edinburgh; 12 Housekeeper; 13 Cook; 14 Kitchen maid; 15 Factory.

LINKS WITH LITERACY

These worksheets take into account the recommended stages of literacy for Years 5 and 6, as outlined in the recent National Literacy Strategy.

A range of strategies relating to fiction and poetry can also be covered, using some of the material and sources contained in both the worksheets and the fiction books on the recommended list on page 6. Non-fiction support and class readers are included in this list.

Extracts from noted works can be used as a literary extension to many of the worksheets, for example Dickens' Oliver Twist with Worksheet 8: Workhouse life; Thomas Hughes' Tom Brown's Schooldays with Worksheet 13: Education for all?; novels by Thomas Hardy for details of agricultural and village life.

Some of the extended written tasks on the sheets can be completed on a wordprocessor and some of the statistics, at present in chart form, can be transposed to computer graphics. Extension tasks to introduce or reinforce some of these specific skills can be provided by the class teacher.

LINKS WITH NUMERACY

At the time of writing, the specific national requirements for numeracy had not been published. However, several of the worksheet activities require numeracy work.

TOPIC PLANNING: CROSS-CURRICULAR LINKS

TECHNOLOGY
- Design a Victorian toy.
- Design a simple machine to transfer motion using a belt, cogs or gears.
- Design a set of clothes for 'Sunday best' for each of the social classes.
- Design and make a 'Sunday best' hat or bonnet.
- Design a Victorian bathing costume to protect the wearer's modesty.
- Design and make a model of a bathing machine.

SCIENCE
- Study of different sources of power developed in 19th century and their uses in industry and transport.

ART
- Study of Victorian artists and photographers. Pupils could study images closely for information about dress, forms of transport, shops, leisure activities, etc.
- Different types of illustration, e.g. cartoons, posters, advertisements.

ENGLISH
- Writing for different purposes, e.g. reports, advertisements, letters, cartoons, posters.
- Poems e.g. life in the workhouse, walking to work in a smoky factory town, a day trip to the seaside/ seeing the sea for the first time.
- Write a Victorian hymn (this could be set to music).

INFORMATION TECHNOLOGY
- Carry out a survey of pupils, parents, etc, based on the census questions devised in Worksheet 2. Create a database. Analyse and present results.

MUSIC
- Study of contemporary composers.
- Study of contemporary popular music and music hall, e.g. Gilbert and Sullivan (this could link with Drama as an extended project to produce a music hall show).
- Compose a hymn tune (see English) or popular song.

Victorian Times

GEOGRAPHY
- Geographical skills linked to town planning, census questionnaire.
- Map skills linked to town planning.

MATHS
- Statistics, based on census material
- Percentages
- Basic arithmetic
- Pictographs
- Measuring and planning, linked to mapping.

DRAMA
- Role play, e.g. landlord, labourer, families in workhouse.
- Production of Victorian melodrama or music hall show (long-term project).

MORAL EDUCATION
- The rise of Non-Conformist religions.
- The moral issues related to the workhouse.
- The differences in education provision for the social classes.
- The plight of the poor in general.
- The rise of organizations such as Barnardo's, Salvation Army.
- Empathy with separated families.
- Where was the Christian spirit?

Further Information

You should be able to find in your local reference library written material such as census material, street directories, etc., related to your own geographical area, and copies of local newspapers on microfilm. It is a good idea to check that your library is prepared to allow children to work on the microfilm readers. Another good source for teachers is the County Record Office. This may hold details about your school, especially the log books, which are an excellent source of information. For simple instructions on how to use the local record office see History Detective Investigates Local History by Martin Parsons (Wayland, 1997).

Two 20-minute videos, A Day in the Life of the Bunce Family (1881), which deals with aspects of Victorian rural life and A Day in the Life of the Bunce and Lyford Families (1891), dealing with town life, offer two distinct case studies. They are professionally produced and all the material in them is historically accurate, having been based on documentary evidence available to the production team. These are available from Pat Parry, Department of Arts and Humanities in Education, University of Reading (tel: 01189 318837 for further details).

NON-FICTION BOOKS SUITABLE FOR KEY STAGE 2 PUPILS

A Victorian Workhouse by John Barwell (Wayland, 1994)
A Victorian Sunday by Simon and Lucy Faulkner (Wayland, 1993)
A Victorian Factory by Lynn Gash and Sheila Watson (Wayland, 1993)
A Victorian Village by Martin Parsons (Wayland, 1995)
Victorian Transport by Katrina Siliprandi (Wayland, 1993)
Learning and Teaching in Victorian Times by P. Speed (Longman, 1988)
Rubbish by G. Tanner (A & C Black, 1991)
History Mysteries: At School by G. Tanner and T. Wood (A & C Black, 1992)
A Victorian Holiday by Sheila Watson (Wayland, 1993)
A Victorian School by Richard Wood (Wayland, 1993)

FICTION BOOKS SUITABLE FOR KEY STAGE 2 PUPILS

Elizabeth Fry and the Forger's Daughter by Roy Apps (Macdonald Young Books, 1996)
Escape From the Workhouse by Patricia Barnard (Anglia, 1989)
Stand Up, Mr Dickens by Edward Blishen (Orion, 1995)
Arthur and the Belly Button Diamond by Alan Coren (Robson, 1979)
Pickwick Papers by Charles Dickens (Penguin, 1997)
Hard Times by Charles Dickens (Penguin, 1995)
Great Expectations by Charles Dickens (Penguin, 1969)
Smith by Leon Garfield (Puffin, 1994)
The Railway Phantoms by Dennis Hamley (Hippo, 1995)
The Golden Key by Mary Hooper (Watts, 1996)
The Sewer Sleuth by Julia Jarman (Watts, 1998)
Convict by Julia Jarman (Watts, 1998)
Lady Daisy by Dick King-Smith (Puffin, 1993)
Christmas Carol by Shiela Lane and Marion Kemp (Ward Lock, 1986)
Oliver Twist by Shiela Lane and Marion Kemp (Ward Lock, 1986)
Tom's Midnight Garden by Philippa Pearce (Puffin, 1976)
The World According to Dickens by Mike Russell (Collins, 1993)
The World According to Hardy by Roger Samways (Collins, 1993)
Chimney Child by Laurie Sheehan (Anglia Young Books, 1998)
Queen Victoria's Swing by Karen Wallace (Harper Collins, 1996)
The Princess and the Parlour Maid by Jeanne Willis (Macdonald Young Books, 1996)
Tom's Lady of the Lamp by Jeanne Willis (Macdonald Young Books, 1995)

Glossary

Name ....   Date ....

The worksheets contain some words which might be new to you. Use a dictionary to find out the meaning of the words written in CAPITAL LETTERS on your worksheet. Then write the meaning next to the word in the list below. Try to explain the word in as much detail as possible. One of them has been done for you, as an example.

AGRICULTURAL LABOURER A farm worker.

CENSUS . . . .

. . . .

ELOCUTION . . . .

. . . .

EXTRACT . . . .

. . . .

FEES . . . .

. . . .

GOVERNESS . . . .

. . . .

LANDLORD . . . .

. . . .

MASS-PRODUCED . . . .

. . . .

PEAT . . . .

. . . .

PROSPECTUS . . . .

. . . .

SELF-SUFFICIENT . . . .

. . . .

Using the census

Name .... Date ....

This is a simplified EXTRACT from the CENSUS of 1891 for the village of Bradfield.

Road or street name	Name and surname	Relation to head of family	Age	Profession or occupation	Where born
3 Southend Road	George Millson	Head; widower	45	Bricklayer	Berks.Stanford Dingley
	Alice J. Do.	Daughter	17	Housekeeper	Do.
	Ellen L. Do.	Daughter	15		Do.
	George J. Do.	Son	14	Farm labourer	Do.
	Sarah A. Do.	Daughter	12	Scholar	Do.
	Lizzie E. Do.	Daughter	10	Scholar	Do.
	Ruth L. Do.	Daughter	3		Do.
	Esther M. Do.	Daughter	3		Do.

Write the meaning of the words EXTRACT and CENSUS in your Glossary.

Look carefully at the extract and then answer these questions.
1. What is the full address of this location?
2. How many people live in this house?
3. What is their surname?
4. How many members of the family had a job?
5. What was the job of the head of the family?
6. How do we know that George's wife had died?
7. Do you think Alice was paid for being housekeeper?
   Give reasons for your answer.
8. Ruth and Esther are both the same age. What does this suggest?
9. What is the difference in age between Alice and Esther?

Wayland
worksheets

Planning the census

Name ....   **Date** ....

Your group has been given the job of designing a new census to find out information about your local area in the year 2011. You will need to get the same information as the 1891 census, but what other information do you think would be useful to planners of towns and roads, or the builders of hospitals, shops or schools in the twenty-first century? Here are some ideas.

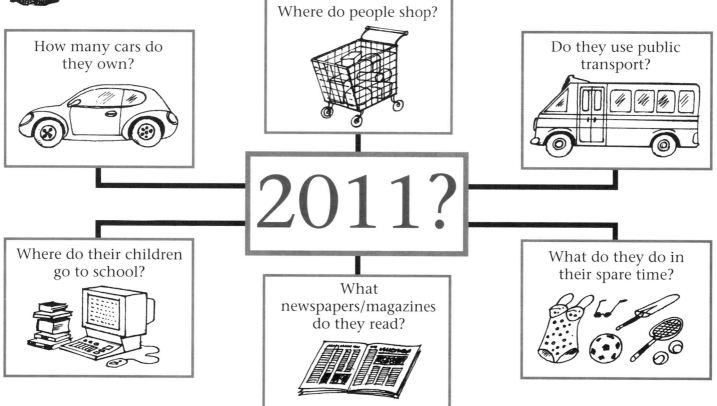

Where do people shop?

How many cars do they own?

Do they use public transport?

2011?

Where do their children go to school?

What newspapers/magazines do they read?

What do they do in their spare time?

1. Make a list of your ideas, then write down the questions you need to ask to get this information.

2. Design a questionnaire.

3. Try out your questionnaire on members of the class to see if they can understand your questions.

Street directories

Name .... **Date** ....

This is a page from a street directory. It gives us information about the Grassmarket area of Edinburgh in 1882–3. (The numbers refer to the number of the house.)

1. Richardson, Francis and Co.

5. Scott, James, and Co.

7. Lindsay, John

9. Spence, Joseph, saddler

11 & 13. Spence, Henry B.

15. Traynor, John, rag merchant

19. McCallum, Alexander Inglis

23. Moyes, James

25. Croan, James

25. Birnie, Patrick, Horse dealer

25. Ritchie, George

27. Steedman, Adam.

31. Main, A & J & Co.
    Corn Exchange Buildings.

60. M'Donald, Angus, saddler

58. Rose, William, saddler

56. Edinburgh Rope, Bag and Twine Store.

54. Wilkinson, John

54. Thomson's Court

54. M'Ewan, Robert

52. Forgan, David, grocer

50. Weir, John

48. Binnie. A., Spirit. Dlr.

46. Kerr. A., Temperance Hotel

44. Wardale, T., & Son. Sawmakers

42. Hume, Elliot, drysalter

42. McCrae, George, Hatter.

Use the information above to answer these questions.

1. Who lived at number 50?
2. How many people in this area had jobs dealing with horses?
3. Can you name them?
4. Why would a 'rag merchant' be important?
5. Can you think of at least two things that these rags could have been used for?
6. Can you find out:
   • what a temperance hotel was?
   • what a 'drysalter' did?

Use other books and a dictionary to help you.

WAYLAND worksheets

Changes

Name ....

Date ....

Historians can look at street directories produced over a number of years to see how an area has changed over time. They can find out which houses have different people living in them and can look at changes in the types of trade. The lists below are extracts from street directories for the Granton area of Edinburgh.

Granton 1881–82 (Cramond District)	Granton 1882–83 (Cramond District)	Granton 1883–84 (Cramond District)
Forth Place	**Forth Place**	**Forth Place**
Duncan, John, Maclean Cottage	Duncan, John, Maclean Cottage	Duncan, John, Maclean Cottage
5. Hartvig, Michael	3. Henderson, David	1. Paulin, John.Coal mer.
3. Henderson, David	2. Blair, John	2. Blair, John
2. Blair, John	Malcolm, D.B., Wardie Hotel	4. Clephane, E.
Malcolm, D.B., Wardie Hotel		5. Allan, David
		Malcolm, D. B., Wardie Hotel, Fort Corinthian Yacht Club
East Cottages	**East Cottages**	**East Cottages**
M'Adie, Robert (H.M.C.)	M'Adie, Robert (H.M.C.)	M'Adie, Robert (H.M.C.)
Geddes, John, shore dues collector	Geddes, John, shore dues collector	Macdonald, Donald, boatman
Macdonald, Donald, boatman	Macdonald, Donald, boatman	M'Kelvie, Archibald
M'Kelvie, Archibald	M'Kelvie, Archibald	Scott, Miss C.
M'Kelvie, Mrs, refreshment rooms	Scott, Miss C.	M'Adie, George (H.M.C.)
M'Adie, George (H.M.C.)	M'Adie, George (H.M.C.)	Scott, W., Ship carpenter
Scott, W., Ship carpenter	Scott, W., Ship carpenter	Landles, George (H.M.C.)
Landles, W., Timber measurer	Landles, W., Timber measurer	Landles, W., Timber measurer
Morrison, Captain William	Reid, A., contractor	Reid, A., contractor
	Morrison, Captain William	Morrison, Captain William

11

Changes

Name .... **Date** ....

Use the information on Worksheet 4A to answer these questions.

1. How many people had moved **away from** this area between 1881 and 1884?

2. How many people had moved **to** the area between 1881 and 1884?

3. How could we find out if George and W. Landles were related? What oth[er] document would we have to look at?

4. How could we find out whether Mrs M'Kelvie who owned the refreshme[nt] rooms in 1881–82 was Archibald M'Kelvie's mother or his wife?

5. What did part of the Wardie Hotel become in 1883–84?

6. From the information in this document, do you think Granton was in th[e] country, in the city or on the coast? Give reasons for your answer.

7. Use a dictionary to find out what the letters H.M.C. stand for.

Imagine you are an estate agent trying to sell Mrs. M'Kelvie's refreshment room in 1883. Design a sales poster and write a description of the property, saying why you think people should buy it. You can make up your own description of:

- what the building was like
- the type of food that was sold there
- the type of people who used it.

The labourer's life

Name .... Date ....

The lives of AGRICULTURAL LABOURERS were often hard. Many lived in houses that had only a single room downstairs, with a kitchen area under the stairs and one bedroom upstairs. The toilet was at the bottom of the garden in a small shed. In the early Victorian period many houses were built of wood because only the wealthy could afford to build houses of stone or brick. However, by 1880 bricks were being MASS-PRODUCED by machines and they became cheaper to buy. This is why many homes from that time onwards were built of brick.

Labourers did not own their own cottages but rented them from a LANDLORD. The rent was around 1 shilling (5p) a week. Although this seems a small amount to pay, you have to remember that labourers only earned about 7 shillings (35p) a week. Children as young as 7 or 8 were employed to scare the crows away from the crops and for this they could earn 5p a week!

During the busy harvest period a labourer could earn £6–8 for a few weeks' work, and the women earned extra money working in the fields. However, when some farmers began to use machinery powered by steam they no longer needed so many workers. The labourers' wages dropped to £3 for the harvest period.

Some people decided that life on the farm in Britain was becoming too difficult. Many people left the country to go to North America, Australia and New Zealand in search of work.

The labourer's life

Name .... **Date** ....

Write the meaning of the words MASS-PRODUCED and LANDLORD in your Glossary.(AGRICULTURAL LABOURER has been done for you.)

Use the information on Worksheet 5A to answer the following questions in **full sentences.**

1. Why were very few labourers' homes built of brick or stone in early Victorian times?

2. What happened in 1880 to make bricks cheaper?

3. What **percentage** of a labourer's wages was spent on the rent?

4. Why did some labourers leave Britain and go to find jobs in other countries?

5. If people could not afford to go to other countries, where else do you think they could have found work? Give reasons for your answer.

6. What did some farmers begin to use which meant that many labourers were put out of work?

7. Who owned the labourer's cottage?

8. What else could a labourer lose if he lost his job?

9. Why were children employed to scare off the birds?

Draw and label a labourer's cottage.

Counting the pennies

Name ....

Date ....

This is a weekly shopping bill and the weekly rent paid by a labourer and his family in the 1850s. The average wage for a labourer was 35p a week.

Clothes were mended and changed many times until they wore out completely. If you look at the costs you can see why few could afford to buy new clothes.

Item	Quantity	Cost (old money)	Cost (decimal)
Bread	5 loaves	2s 6d	12½p
Potatoes	3 pecks*	1s 6d	7½p
Bacon	½ lb	3½d	1½p
Salt	¼d worth	¼d	
Tea	¼ oz	1d	½p
Soap	5 lb	3d	1½p
Candles	¼ lb	1½d	¾p
Coal	½ cwt**	5d	2½p
PEAT	1d worth	1d	½p
Rent		1s 6d	7½p
Total		6s 9¼d	34¾p

* 1 peck = 8 quarts (13.5 litres) of dry measure
** 1 cwt = 112 lb (1 lb = 454 g)

Farmer's smock
2s 6d
(12½p)

Shirt
1s (5p)

Trousers
1s (5p)

Boots
5s (25p)

Write the meaning of the word PEAT in your Glossary.

Now answer these questions.

1. If a labourer only had one farthing (quarter of a penny) left at the end of the week, how long would it take him to save up for a new pair of boots? (Every shilling was worth 12 old pennies.)

2. Why do you think the labourer's family used 5 pounds of soap every week?

3. Why do you think they ate so many potatoes and loaves of bread?

4. If 1 hundredweight = 112 pounds, how many kilograms does this represent?

15

WAYLAND worksheets

Village trades

Name ....   Date ....

OCCUPATIONS

Trade
Bricklayer (2)
Draper (2)
Carrier/Coal Merchant (5)
Gas Man (1)
Builder (1)
Needlewoman (1)
Carpenter/Joiner (12)
Broom Maker (1)
Baker/Grocer (9)
Grocer's Assistant (2)
Tanner (2)
Decorator (2)
Dressmaker (1)
Innkeeper (4)
Blacksmith (5)
Bootmaker (4)
Tailor (1)
Tailor's Apprentice (1)
Wheelwright (1)

General
Labourer (69)
Capt. Royal Artillery (1)
Army Pensioner (1)
Pedlar's Hawker (2)
Soda Water Bottler (1)
Engine Fitter (1)
Postmaster (1)
Postal Clerk (4)
Postman (1)
Police Constable (1)

Mineral Waterman & Fly
   Owner (1)
Engineer in Steam Laundry (1)
Stationary Engine Driver (1)

Agriculture
Labourers (77)
Watercress Grower (2)
Market Gardener (2)
Hay Dealer (1)
Milk Boy (1)
Stable Boy (1)
Fruit Grower (1)
Dairyman (3)
Dairywoman (1)
Farm Bailiff (3)
Shepherd (4)
Cowman (3)
Farmers (18)
Farm Boy (2)
Carter (10)

Education
Scholar (177)
Schoolmaster (2)
Teacher (3)
Maths Student (1)

Professional
Physician (1)
Registrar (4)
Surveyor (1)
Electrical Engineer

Rector (1)
Methodist Minister (1)
Barrister (1)
Midwife (1)

Domestic
Servants (48)
Housekeeper (8)
Groom (4)
Gardener (13)
Laundress (17)
Washer Woman (1)
Mother's Help (2)
Charwoman (2)
Butler (3)
Housemaid (5)
Kitchenmaid (1)
Coachman (6)
Footman (3)
Governess (5)
Nurse (3)
Nursegirl (1)
Nursemaid (2)
Parlourmaid (2)
Cook (4)
Under-domestic (1)
House-boy

Estate
Gamekeeper (4)
Under-keeper (1)
Land Agent (1)
Woodsman (2)

Village trades

Name ....   **Date** ....

Worksheet 7A gives details of the people who lived in a small village in West Berkshire in the 1880s. Its population was about 1,000 people. You can see that everybody in the village had a trade or profession, or worked on the local farms or in the big houses, or went to the local school. Many villages were SELF-SUFFICIENT like this.

Write the meaning of the word SELF-SUFFICIENT in your Glossary.

Now answer these questions, using the information on Worksheet 7A.

1. What **percentage** of people in this village worked in agriculture?

2. How many churches do you think there were in this village?

3. Using other books in your library, find out:
   • what a 'fly' was
   • what job a farm bailiff did
   • what a draper sold
   • what a woodsman did.

4. There were 5 teachers and 177 'scholars' (pupils) in this village. What was the **ratio** of teachers to pupils?

5. How does this compare with the number of teachers and pupils in your school today?

6. What **percentage** of the population was involved in labouring or listed as servants?

7. Draw a **pictograph** to show the number of people in the village who worked in trades.

17

Workhouse life

Name ....

Date ....

You are going to write a script for a radio documentary about workhouses.

1.   Decide what you should include in your report. Each person can be responsible for a topic, for example, diet, conditions, etc.

2.   Use the information on this sheet **and** details from other books to make notes on each topic. Remember, you will not be able to show pictures, so you will have to use words very clearly to describe what life was like.

3.   When you have made your notes, you can start to write the script for your programme. Make it interesting for the listeners.

4.   Once you have finished the written work, you can record it on to tape. You might like to add sound effects – doors opening, and people crying, snoring, eating, etc., – to bring your description alive.

Who went to the workhouse?
- People who couldn't pay their rent and were thrown out of their homes.
- Widows, orphans and people too old to work.

What was the workhouse like?
- High walls, big gates and very small windows.
- Separate sections for men and women, so families had to be split up. In some workhouses even the chapel had separate sections.

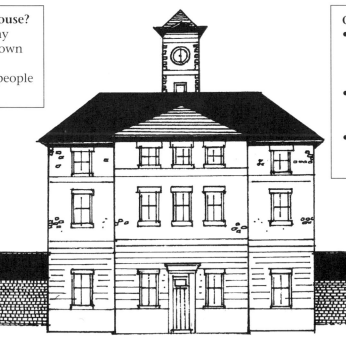

Children
- Children over one year old were taken from their mothers and looked after in a children's section.
- They had lessons for part of the day in the workhouse or local school.
- Children old enough to work were sent to local farms or factories.

Diet
The food was always the same.
Breakfast
6 oz (175 g) buttered bread
1 pint (0.6 l) of tea
Dinner
4 oz (125 g) bacon
3 oz (75 g) bread or
            potatoes
Supper
6 oz (175 g) bread
1 pint (0.6 l) tea
2 oz (50g) cheese

Conditions
- Harsh, so that people would try to avoid going to the workhouse if they possibly could.
- Strict discipline.
- No talking during meals or work periods.
- When inmates died they were buried in unmarked graves, containing 3–4 other bodies.
- Workhouses did not close until the 1930s!

The growing towns

Name ....

Date ....

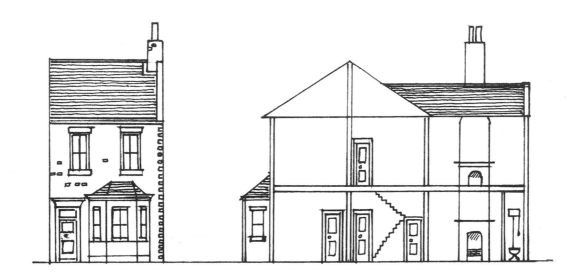

Many people came to the factory towns to find work, so the population grew quickly. The population of Manchester in 1801 was 75,000 but in 1851 it was 303,000! Town planners found it very difficult to provide the houses and other services that people needed. Living conditions for factory workers were very hard.

Imagine you have rented the house shown here. You have six children – four girls aged 8, 10, 11 and 16, and two boys aged 4 and 9. You are also looking after your elderly mother who can no longer go out to work, so with you and your husband/wife there are three adults in the family. How are you going to fit everybody in?

1. Where would everybody sleep?
2. Remember there is no bathroom – where would everybody bathe?
3. Make a list of the furniture you would buy for each room.

What services do you need now that you have settled in your home? Where will you get food and water? What will you do if one of your children becomes ill?

Town planning

Name .... Date ....

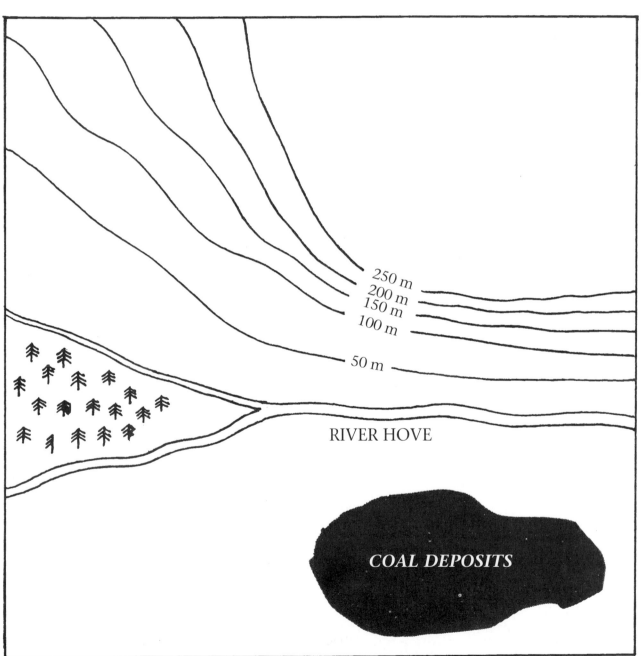

250 m
200 m
150 m
100 m

50 m

RIVER HOVE

COAL DEPOSITS

Town planning

Name ....   **Date** ....

Look at the map on Worksheet 10A. It shows an area in Britain during the early Victorian period. There is a river, and coal deposits, hills and forests. It would be a good place to set up a factory. You are going to decide how the town will grow.

Map symbols

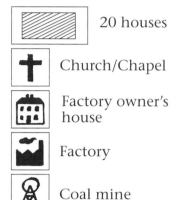

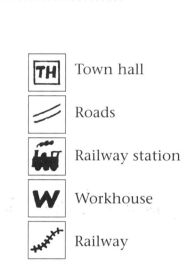

▨ 20 houses	S School	TH Town hall
✝ Church/Chapel	H Hospital	⁄ Roads
🏠 Factory owner's house	🍺 Public house	🚂 Railway station
🏭 Factory	😀 Theatre	W Workhouse
Coal mine	Shop	Railway

FOLLOW THE INSTRUCTIONS IN THE CORRECT ORDER AND USE THE CORRECT SYMBOLS. DRAW EVERYTHING IN PENCIL. YOUR DRAWINGS MUST BE THE SAME SIZE AS THE SYMBOLS. REMEMBER:
- You can only build two bridges across the river but these can be built at any time.
- You can cut down the trees whenever you like.
- The river floods during winter.

1. Draw on your map: 5 blocks of 20 houses, 2 coal mines, 1 factory, 1 factory owner's house, 2 shops, 1 school, 1 church, 1 public house.

2. Add 10 blocks of 20 houses, 2 coal mines, 1 theatre, 3 factories, 3 factory owners' houses, 1 town hall, 5 shops, 4 public houses.

3. Add 10 blocks of 20 houses, 3 factories, 3 public houses, 5 shops.

4. Add 10 blocks of 20 houses, 2 factories, 15 shops, 1 workhouse.

5. It is now after 1840. Add railway lines and a station, and some roads. (You may need to knock down some houses to fit these in.)

6. Provide a water supply and sewage pipes to houses, factories, etc. (Draw the pipes on in blue.) Add a hospital. Knock down houses and/or factories if necessary.

Town planning

Name .... **Date** ....

Put the following buildings on a blank copy of Worksheet 10A, IN ANY ORDER:

- 40 blocks of 20 houses
- 6 coal mines
- 10 factories
- 5 factory owners' houses
- 29 shops
- 2 schools
- 2 churches
- 9 public houses

- 1 theatre
- 1 town hall
- 1 workhouse
- 1 hospital
- 1 railway station
- railway lines
- roads
- water and sewage pipes

1. Compare your two plans. Are there any differences? Did you have to knock down any houses in your second plan?

2. If you were a real town planner, which method would you use? Would you add buildings as more people arrived, OR would you have an overall plan before you began to build?

3. Which method do you think some of the Victorian planners used? Give reasons for your answer.

22

Servants wanted

Name ....   **Date** ....

1. You have just moved to a large house and you wish to employ a **cook** and a **kitchen maid**. Write an advertisement for each job to go in the newspaper. Remember to make the job sound really good so that you will get lots of applicants.

Kitchen maid
Did the dirty jobs, such as:
• washing-up, using washing soda which made her hands very sore
• cleaning chopping boards
• cutting and pounding up sugar and salt from large blocks
• cleaning fish
• plucking chickens, pheasants and other birds
• cleaning copper pans using silver sand, vinegar and salt. Lemon was also used to clean very detailed moulds for the jellies and other foods.
The kitchen maid usually prepared the servants' meals, too, and was the last to be served at mealtimes.

Housekeeper
Organized the servants and made sure the house was run properly. She did the household accounts, and tasks such as making special cakes, jellies, jams or ice-creams.

2. Imagine you have just started work as a kitchen maid. You don't really want to work as a servant but your parents cannot afford to keep you any longer. Write a letter home to your parents telling them what your job is like.

The cook's day

Name .... **Date** ....

Use the information below to create a cartoon strip showing 'A Day in the Life of a Cook'. Think about what you will need to show in each picture. What characters do you need to draw? How will you show what time of day it is? Can you put any of the information into speech bubbles?

6.15 am	Woken up by kitchen maid.
7.00 am	Bake bread rolls and prepare the hot dishes for the family breakfast.
7.45 am	Put on a clean apron and go upstairs for family prayers with the other servants.
8.00 am	Send up breakfast to the dining room.
8.15 am	Eat breakfast with the other servants.
9.15 am	Have meeting with the lady of the house to arrange the meals for the day.
9.30 am	Prepare soups for the next day.
10.30 am	Prepare jellies and creams for the next day and lunch for the family.
12.00 pm	Eat dinner with other servants.
1.00 pm	Send up lunch to the dining room and dinner for the children in the nursery.
2.00 pm	Rest.
3.00 pm	Do household accounts.
4.00 pm	Send up tea to the children in the nursery.
5.00 pm	Send up family tea to the dining room and start preparing dinner.
8.00 pm	Send up dinner to the dining room.
9.00 pm	Eat supper with the other servants.
10.00 pm	Close down the fire. Close windows and doors.
10.30 pm	Go to bed.

Education for all?

Name ....   Date ....

Schools in the nineteenth century were very different from schools today. Education was not compulsory until the 1880s and the working classes learned only the basic 'three Rs' of Reading, wRiting and aRithmetic.

Dame schools
- Run by women, some of whom could not even read themselves.
- Provided education for small groups of children.
- Parents paid the teacher a few pennies.

Ragged schools
- Opened to provide free education for poor children (from 1844, children working in factories had to have six half-days' schooling a week.)

National schools
- Run by church organizations to teach children to read the Bible.
- Held in the church, a person's house or even an old farm building.
- Also known as 'British schools'.

Victorian Education

Grammar schools
- Boys learned Greek and Latin (the Classics).
- Charged parents large FEES.
- Charged extra for lessons such as Science, French and Maths.
- After 1870 some opened separate sections for girls.

Education at home
- Many young upper- and middle-class children were taught at home by a nanny or a GOVERNESS.

Board schools
- Set up after the 1870 Education Act, which stated that schools must be provided for all children aged 5–12.
- Controlled by a Board of Governors.
- At first, parents paid a small fee (School's Pence) each week. Fees were abolished in 1891.

Private schools
- People paid for their children to go to these schools.
- Some schools were very good but others had few books and the lessons were very poor.
- Girls in private schools were taught subjects which the teachers hoped would get them good husbands. These included: Music, Manners, ELOCUTION, Sewing, Art and Cookery.

Public schools
- For boys from around 10 years old until they were 18. After this they went on to university.
- Pupils studied Latin and Greek. Later, new public schools taught Science, Maths, P.E, English and French.

Education for all?

Name .... Date ....

Write the meaning of the words ELOCUTION, FEES and GOVERNESS in your Glossary.

Now answer these questions using the information on Worksheet 13A.

1. Why do you think poor children were only taught the 'three Rs'?

2. Why do you think a factory owner would have found it useful to provide lessons for children working in his factory?

3. If the 'three Rs' were Reading, wRiting and aRithmetic, what do you think the 'fourth R' would have been in a National school?

4. Why do you think middle-class and upper-class families had their young children taught at home?

5. Look carefully at the subjects girls were taught at school.

   • Why do you think these subjects would help girls to 'get a good husband'?

   • Does the list of subjects tell us anything about the kind of life they were expected to lead after they left school?

   • Why do you think few girls went on to university?

Imagine you are the headteacher of either:

   • a Victorian private school for girls, OR

   • a Victorian grammar school for boys.

Design a PROSPECTUS to encourage parents to send their children to your school. (Look up the word PROSPECTUS in a dictionary and add it to your Glossary.) Include details of lessons, sports or other activities, but remember your prospectus must be historically accurate. Look in other books for more information about schools, to help you.

School log book

Name ....

Date ....

Read these extracts from a school log book and then answer the questions.

1883

14 February Small attendance today. Many children went to Bradfield Hall for the usual Valentine's Day gift.

5-7 March Attendance much smaller than usual this week owing to the cold weather.

6 August Very small attendance today because of the Band-of-Hope tea party.

1884

26 June The haymaking having commenced, several children were absent this week.

25 February Received information that a case of smallpox had occurred at Stanford and therefore the children from that district would not be allowed to attend school.

1885

2 March Wet weather. Attendance rather small.

7 September Outbreak of Measles. By order of Dr. Woodford the school was closed until the infection had passed away.

2 November The school was reopened today after 13 weeks.

1886

16 March Rev. J. Wallace gave a Magic Lantern show in the large room this evening to which all the school children were invited. Nearly 200 people were present.

1887

15 March Deep snow. Poor Attendance.

1. Why would the weather make such a difference to the number of children attending school?
2. Look at the extract for 1884. Write down **two** reasons why fewer children attended school during haymaking.
3. Why do you think the school was closed for such a long time because of the measles?
4. What do the extracts tell us about the way doctors prevented such diseases from spreading?
5. What was a Magic Lantern show? What would we call this machine today? How do we know that the Magic Lantern show was a popular event?

Going to church

Name .... **Date** ....

Religion was a very important part of a child's life in Victorian times. Although it was easy to miss church services in the towns, children in villages were punished in school on the Monday for missing Sunday school and church the day before.

Sunday school
Before 1870, the only education some children received was at Sunday school. Some churches gave children prizes for good attendance at Sunday school. Discipline was often strict – some Sunday school teachers used the cane, like teachers in other schools. However, there were benefits, such as Sunday school outings and picnics.

City missions
There was a drop in the number of people going to churches in the towns and cities during the Victorian period. Some people were afraid that poor children would not be taught the difference between right and wrong if they did not go to church. City missions were set up to persuade the poor to go to church services.

Rich and poor
Some of the working classes felt unwelcome at Church of England services. They went to Methodist, Baptist or Congregational chapels instead, where people did not worry about how much money they had or what social class they were from.

Now answer these questions.
1. Why do you think poorer people often felt unwelcome at some Church of England services?
2. You needed to be able to read to join in with the hymns and the readings in church. Why do you think this made it more difficult for the poor to take part in many services?
3. Why was it important for the poorer children to go to Sunday school?

Produce a poster to encourage people to go to a city mission. Can you get your message across using pictures and just a few simple twords?

Ticket to ride

Name ....   **Date** ....

From the 1840s the new railways allowed people to travel greater distances. Early trains were not very comfortable, but travelling on them was relatively cheap. From 1844 railway companies had to provide seats for third-class passengers, with tickets costing 1d (one penny) a mile. Some factory owners paid for their workers to have a day trip to the seaside.

Train travel helped to develop the Victorian seaside resort. If you go to seaside towns today you will see many Victorian buildings and perhaps a pier. At first only the rich could afford to stay at the seaside, in the hotels. Later, cheap lodging houses opened, which allowed poorer people to stay for longer holidays.

Now answer these questions.

1. There were 12 pennies in a shilling. How much would it have cost three adults to make a rail journey of 50 miles, travelling third class?

2. Imagine these three adults were agricultural labourers earning 7 shillings a week. Once they had paid for food, fuel and rent, they each had only a half-penny left over at the end of each week. How long would it have taken them to save up for the journey and have 1 shilling each to spend while they were at the seaside?

3. In the picture below you can see a bathing machine. People changed into their bathing costumes in one of these. Then the 'machine' was pulled into the sea so that the people could walk down the steps straight into the water. What does this tell us about people's attitude to swimming and being seen in bathing costumes?

WAYLAND worksheets

Planning Seathorpe

Name ....   Date ....

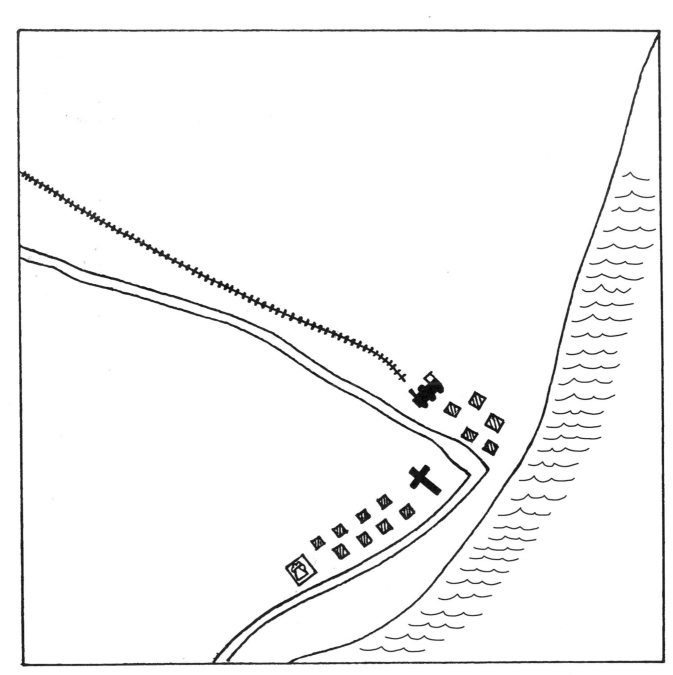

30

House	Pub		
✝ Church	╱ Road		
Railway station	Railway line		

Planning Seathorpe

Name ....   Date ....

You are members of the town council of Seathorpe. It is 1842. The railway line has just reached your seaside town and people are coming from the nearby industrial cities every Sunday and at other times during the year. You have been given the job of planning what the town will provide for visitors.

Use these questions to help you decide what to do.
• Where are people going to stay? (Don't forget that you will have to cater for the wealthy as well as the poor.)
• What extra services will you need to provide for people who are staying in the town, or visiting for the day? Not all lodging houses provided meals, so where will people eat?
• What entertainments do you want to provide? Will there be places for people to go when it is raining?
• Can you think of a new and unusual attraction to bring people to Seathorpe? (In Blackpool, for example, they built the Tower; some towns built piers.)
• Will you need to employ extra people during the holiday season to look after the trippers?
• What types of souvenir will you sell? Again, remember that there will be rich and poor visitors.

1. Mark on the map the new buildings, attractions and services that you are going to add to the town.

2. Draw some pictures of the souvenirs you will sell.

3. On a large sheet of paper design an eye-catching poster to be put up in the railway stations in the industrial towns, advertising Seathorpe. It should include all the new features that you have planned to attract holiday-makers.

Revision wordsearch

Name .... Date ....

```
E K S T R E E T D I R E C T O R I E S A
E I F H G Z Y L P T T I F A C T O R Y G
M T A A R Q K N I F E B O Y E D A L I R
I C T M A N C H E S T E R Z N S B O P I
G H T U D P E O P L E D S O S V L C X C
R E I N M I H Y M N A L T J U S T I N U
A N L D K Q U P A U L H E T S N Y F N L
N M M E P U N I P S W O R K H O U S E T
T A N L A N D L O R D U K N A R F P W U
R I C L E A R N T T O S I N G Y B O Z R
A D D A X Y E A R S K E E P E R O A E A
I O O L M A D U N W I T T I N G B C A L
N W N R P E S T E R D E T E R E D H L L
E D I N B U R G H A A U S T R A L I A A
N O R T H U M I L T M P C O O K A N N B
B U S R A G G E D F E C H O R D U G D O
U B T U M I M L F A S B O A R D D O M U
R L A X U K N P E S C H O O L L A D A R
S E M Y R O X G T R D E L I G H T Y R E
T O P I C T E S T I M O N Y O Z E P Y R
```

Can you find these hidden words?

1. Two countries that people went to live in overseas.
2. The name given to people who went to live overseas.
3. Two types of school.
4. A person who rented out land.
5. Another name for farm workers.
6. A city where the population rose by over 200,000 in fifty years.
7. Useful documents for finding out what buildings were used for in the past.
8. A survey carried out every ten years.
9. The length of time before the public can look at the information from a census.
10. The place where poor people ended up if they lost their job and house.
11. The capital of Scotland.
12. The person in charge of the accounts and servants.
13. The person in charge of the food in a large house.
14. The servant who did the dirtiest jobs in the kitchen.
15. A place where things were mass produced.